RESCUE!

Contents

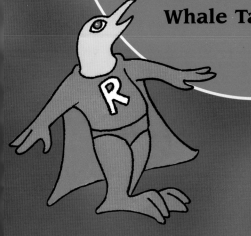

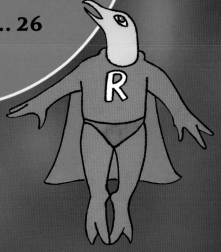

It Wasn't a Trick

Written by Sharon Capobianco   Illustrated by Kelvin Hawley

It was April 15, 1912.
It was very late at night.
The radio man on the ship the *Carpathia*
was going to shut off the radio.
Then he was going to go to bed.

But then a message came in.
The message was from the *Titanic*.
The *Titanic* was the biggest ship
of the day.
It was on its first trip to America.

The radio man read the message.
The message said
that the *Titanic* had hit an iceberg.
The *Titanic* was badly damaged.

This could not be true.
The *Titanic* could not sink!

The radio man
sent a message back to the *Titanic*.
Then he ran
to tell the officer on watch.

The officer on watch
did not think that the message
from the *Titanic* was right.
He could see the lights of the *Titanic*.
He thought that the message was a trick.
He didn't think
that the *Titanic* needed help.

Why do you think
the officer on watch
thought that
the message was
a trick?

The radio man knew what he had to do.
He would have to tell the captain.
And that was just what he did.

"Here is a message from the *Titanic*,"
the radio man said.
"The *Titanic* has hit an iceberg.
It is going to sink!"

The captain did not think
that the message was a trick.
He knew that icebergs were in the water.
He knew that you could only see
a small part of the iceberg.
The rest of the iceberg was under the water.
He made the ship turn around
and go and help the *Titanic*.

The *Carpathia*
went as fast as it could.
It went to help the *Titanic*.
The *Carpathia*
sent fire rockets into the air.
The *Titanic*
could see that help
was on the way.

The *Carpathia*
got there at four o'clock in the morning.
Its crew rescued as many as 705 people.

When the *Carpathia* got to New York,
a very special person came to visit them.
The person was Guglielmo Marconi.
Guglielmo Marconi made the first radio.
He came to tell the radio men
what a good job they had done.

Now radios on ships
are open all the time.
If the radio man on the *Titanic*
had called the *Carpathia* any later,
it would have been too late.
If the *Carpathia*
had not come,
all the people on the *Titanic*
would have died.

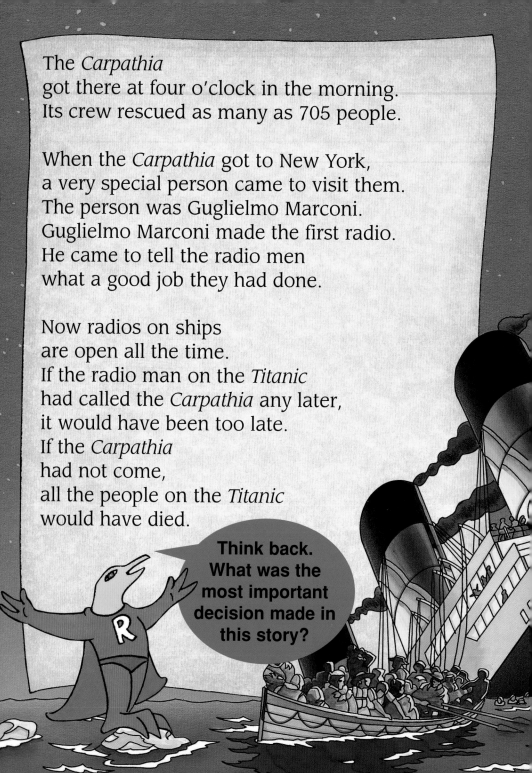

**Think back.
What was the
most important
decision made in
this story?**

The Building Site

Written by Judy Ling   Illustrated by Marjorie Scott

Jordan did not like it
when there was no school.
His mother had to work,
so he had to go to Grandma King's place.

Grandma King lived in their building.
She lived on her own.
There was nothing to do at her place.
And he was told that he could not go
to the building site.

But Jordan loved the building site.
It was full of junk from old buildings.
The sign said,
Danger! Keep Out!
But Jordan wanted to go in.

"There's nothing for me to do,"
Jordan said to Grandma King.

"You can go and get some bread for me,"
said Grandma King.

Jordan went past the building site.
A girl was jumping up and down
on a pile of dirt and rocks.

Just then the dirt and rocks
started to move.

"Look out!" Jordan yelled.

The girl didn't hear him.

Why should you never go onto a building site?

"Get out!" Jordan yelled.
He saw the girl fall down.
The dirt and rocks fell on top of her.

Jordan got over the fence to get to the girl.
He dug into the dirt and rocks until his fingers hurt.
He kept on digging some more.

He dug until he got the dirt and rocks
away from the girl's mouth and nose.
Then he looked to see if she was breathing.
The girl was breathing,
but she did not look very good.
He had to get help.
If he moved the girl, he might hurt her more.

So he got back over the fence
and ran to a telephone.
On the way, he yelled out, "Help, help!"
But no one was there.

Jordan called the emergency number.
"Please come to the corner of 1st and 41st,"
Jordan yelled.
"A girl has been hurt at a building site."

"Someone will be there very soon,"
the man said.

Jordan got back just as the police car came.
It stopped beside him.
A policewoman jumped out.

"She's down there," Jordan said.

A policeman asked Jordan for his phone number.
Jordan gave him his mother's work number.

Soon the paramedics came.
They carried the girl out on a stretcher.

"We'll take you to the hospital, too,"
said one of the paramedics.
"Your hands don't look very good."

Jordan looked at the blood all over his hands.

At the hospital, a nurse bandaged Jordan's hands.

Then Jordan's mother came.
"Jordan!" she said.
"Are you all right?
Does it hurt?
What did you do?"

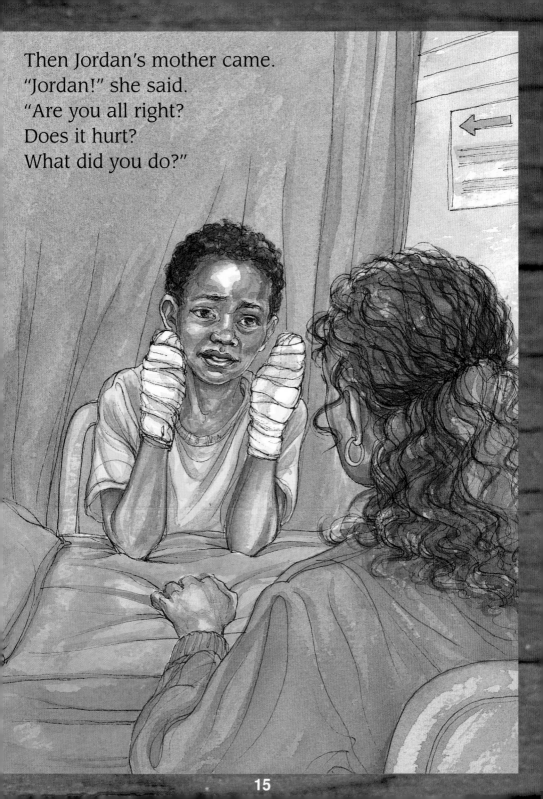

"I dug a girl out of the building site," Jordan said.
"Then I ran to get help."

Jordan's mother gave him a hug.
"You're a great kid," she said.

A woman came up to them.

"You must be Jordan," the woman said.
"I've seen you at Grandma King's place.
I'm Harlene's mother.
Thank you for saving her."

"Is she all right?" Jordan asked.

"Yes," said the woman, "thanks to you.
Would Jordan like to come over some time
and use the computer?" she asked Jordan's mother.

"Say yes," said Jordan. "Please!"

"Well . . ." said Jordan's mother, " . . . all right."

"Cool!" said Jordan.

Now he would like it
when school was out!

Do you know what to do in an emergency?

Kate to the Rescue

Written by Alison Condon   Illustrated by Maggie Dannatt

"Dad, can I drive the racing car?" said Kate.

"No, Kate, you are too young," said her dad.
"Racing cars are too fast.
You can sit on the bank and watch."

Kate sat on the bank.
She loved the bright red car
with the big black wheels.
She would love to drive her dad's car.
Maybe one day
her dad would let her go for a ride with him.

Kate's dad got into the car.
He put on his racing harness.
He put on his hard hat.

"Would you like to use the stopwatch?" said Pete.
Pete looked after her dad's car.
He made sure that the car was all right to race.

"Yes," said Kate, and she held the stopwatch
in one hand and the starting flag in the other.
"Go," she called and dropped the flag.

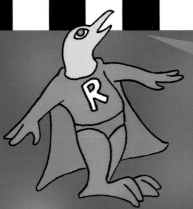

How fast do you think the car is going?

Dad was off.
He zoomed around the track.

After five laps, Kate waved the flag
and stopped the watch.
"You did that in good time," she called,
and she held up the stopwatch for her dad to see.

"But I can go faster," said Dad.
"I'll take one more ride."

"Be careful, Dad," said Kate.
"You were going really fast,
but the back wheels didn't look very good."

"Yes," said Pete.
"Kate's right,
those back wheels don't look very good."

"I'll be fine," said Dad.
"Here I go."

Off he went around and around the track.

"Wow!" said Kate.
"Dad is really going fast."

Then the car turned.
It slid to the side.

"Look out!" yelled Pete.

Kate and Pete saw the car slide off the track.
Then the car rolled over and over.

Kate and Pete ran to the racing car.
It was on its roof.

"Dad, are you all right?" cried Kate.

Kate's dad didn't move.
Then he slowly lifted his hand.

"My belt is stuck," he said, "so I can't get it off."

"I've got a knife," said Pete.
He tried to get to the belt, but he couldn't get it.

"I'll have to get help," he said to Kate and her dad.

Then Kate saw smoke.

"The car," she cried.
"There is smoke coming out of Dad's car."

Kate picked up the knife
before Pete could stop her.
She got through the window of the car.

"Get out, Kate," said Dad. "It's not safe."

But Kate kept on cutting the belt with the knife.
At last, the belt gave way.
Then Kate pulled and pulled on the door,
but it wouldn't open.

Just then some men came to help her.
Pete and some paramedics came running, too.
The paramedics got Kate's dad out of the car.

"Thanks for saving me, Kate," Dad said to Kate.
He held onto her hand.

"That's all right, Dad," said Kate.

"When I'm well," Dad said,
"you can help Pete look after the car.
You will be able to find out a lot about cars.
And then one day,
you will be able to race cars like me."

And he smiled a big smile at Kate.

Why could Kate cut her dad free when Pete couldn't?

Whale Tale

Written by Paul Reeder   Illustrated by Falcon Halo

It had been a very hot day.
Some whales had come onto the sand.
And we were going to the beach to help them.

At the beach,
there were lots and lots of whales
on the sand.
It was very sad to see.

We asked a woman which whales to help.
She told us to go and help the people
who were looking
after three big whales.

Dad said, "Don't run around.
You must stay with us."

The whales didn't look well.
The whales looked very hot.
The woman told us
to keep the whales wet.

Why did Dad say, "Don't run around?"

I used a bucket to put water on the whales.
I had to run down to the sea to fill it up.
My mother and father helped, too.
A man had a big bucket.
He was putting water on the whales.
A boy and girl were digging around the whales.
The water was filling up the hole.

"Why did the whales come here?" I asked.

"Sometimes, the whales
get too close to the land.
Then they don't know
where they are going," said a man.

"One whale may have come onto the sand.
It may have called to the other whales.
The other whales came to help it.
They came onto the sand, too,"
said a woman.

"Soon the tide will come in,"
said the man.
"Then we can help
the whales get
back into the sea."

Why do whales get stranded on beaches?

The tide came in.

"Sometimes the whales
come back out of the water,"
said the woman.
"So stay with your whale if it is in the water!"

My mother and father
stayed with one of the whales.
I went onto the sand.
Some people were in boats.
They were helping the whales
swim out to the sea.

But one whale was coming back.
So a boat went up to it.
The people on the boat
had to help the whale turn around.
They helped the whale swim out
to the other whales.

But some whales did not live.
I was very sad about that.
It had been a long, long day.
But I was very happy, too,
because we had helped
lots of whales.

Why did
some of the
whales die?

Glossary

building site – a place where an old building has been pulled down or a new building is being built

emergency number – a telephone number used by people to call for help in an emergency

hard hat – a helmet made to protect the head

iceberg – a floating "mountain" of ice that has broken away from a glacier

paramedics – people who have been trained to help injured or sick people before a doctor can get to them

starting flag – a flag used by the starter of a race to signal to competitors that the race has begun

stopwatch – a watch that can be started and stopped to record time, and that can be used by people to find out how long a race or event takes

WILDCATS™

Tiger

Sports and Action

A Division of The **McGraw·Hill** Companies

Mc Graw Hill

**Wright Group
McGraw-Hill**

ISBN: 0-322-00543-4